ease return this bo...

KU-300-819

PLAYS

SPOOKY!

Barbara Mitchelhill

Published in association with
The Basic Skills Agency

Hodder & ...

A MEMBER OF THE HOD...

Acknowledgements
Cover: Stuart Williams
Illustrations: Jim Eldridge

Orders: please contact Bookpoint Ltd, 39 Milton Park, Abingdon, Oxon OX14
4TD. Telephone: (44) 01235 400414, Fax: (44) 01235 400454. Lines are open
from 9.00–6.00, Monday to Saturday, with a 24 hour message answering
service. Email address: orders@bookpoint.co.uk

British Library Cataloguing in Publication Data
A catalogue record for this title is available from The British Library

ISBN 0 340 74323 9

First published 1999
Impression number   10 9 8 7 6 5 4 3 2
Year   2004 2003 2002 2001 2000 1999

Typeset by by Fakenham Photosetting Ltd, Fakenham, Norfolk.
Printed in Great Britain for Hodder & Stoughton Educational, a division of
Hodder Headline Plc, 338 Euston Road, London NW1 3BH by Athenaeum
Press Ltd, Gateshead, Tyne & Wear.

About the play

The People

- **Jess**
- **Ryan**

Brother and sister.

The Time

Eleven o'clock at night.

What's Happening

Jess and *Ryan* *have to spend the night alone in a lonely holiday cottage in Cornwall while their mother visits their sick gran. The telephone starts to ring.*

Act 1

Ryan The phone's ringing.

Jess Mmmm.

Ryan Can't you get it?

Jess Can't you?

I'm reading.

Ryan You're dead lazy, you are!

(*he picks up the phone*)

Hello?

Hi, Mum! How yer doin'?

(*pause*)

Oh, we're all right.

We didn't go out this afternoon.

It's been raining all day.

Rotten holiday weather.

(*pause*)

Yes, we've had tea.

(*pause*)

And we've drawn the curtains.

(*pause*)

And we've locked the doors.

(*pause*)

Yes, we'll go to bed soon.

Honest! We'll be all right.

Jess Let me speak to Mum, Ryan!

Ryan Jess wants a word.

I'll hand you over.

See ya!

Jess   Hi, Mum! How's Gran?

       (*pause*)

       Oh that's good.

       I'm glad she's better.

       So you'll be back in the morning?

       (*pause*)

       Of course we don't mind staying by ourselves.

       It's only for one night.

       (*pause*)

       Yes, we'll take care.

       See you soon. Love to Gran. Bye!

       (*puts phone down*)

Ryan   Mum doesn't like leaving us, does she?

       I bet she thinks this place is haunted.

Jess returns to her seat and picks up her book.

Jess   Well she could be right.

Ryan   What do you mean?

Jess   I mean this house might be haunted.

Ryan   Don't be stupid, Jess.

          What are you talking about?

Jess   This book I'm reading

          – it's all about this house.

          It says there's a ghost.

          It's really SPOOKY!

Ryan   Go on then. Tell me about it.

Jess   Are you sure you can take it?

          Aren't you scared

          – miles away from anywhere?

          Eleven o'clock at night?

          WOOOOOOHHHHH!

Ryan   Don't be stupid, Jess.

          Get on with it!

Jess	Well, the story starts in 1908.
	This house was a farm then.
	It was owned by a rich widow
	called Elizabeth Shaw.
Ryan	What's a widow?
Jess	A woman whose husband has died.
	Don't you know anything?
Ryan	I only asked. No need to be nasty.
	So what about this widow?
	She was rich, was she?
Jess	I said so, didn't I?
	In 1908 she met a man
	called Matthew Roberts
	and she married him.
Ryan	Was he rich?
Jess	No. He was just a farm hand.
Ryan	I bet he was after her money.
Jess	I wonder if that's them
	in that picture up there.
	It looks very old.

Ryan   Never mind pictures.
Get on with the story.

Jess   Elizabeth had a servant
called Annie Harris.
She worked in the house,
doing the cleaning and cooking.
One day,
something terrible happened.

Ryan   What?

Jess   All the silver in the farmhouse
disappeared,
and loads of money.
It was in a chest under the bed.

Ryan   That's a daft place to keep money.

Jess   Yeah. But I suppose they did that
in those days.

Ryan   Who nicked it?

Jess   Everybody said it was the servant.

Ryan   Annie? What did she say about it?

Jess   She didn't say anything.
She disappeared.

Ryan I suppose she ran off
with the money.
Did they catch her?

Jess No. They looked everywhere.
The only clue was found
in a secret passage in the farmhouse.
They found Annie's wool shawl and
a ring which belonged
to the farmer's wife.

Ryan	So that's how she got away.
	Through a secret passage. Cool!
Jess	That's what everybody thought.
	They thought she'd got away.
	But her ghost came back
	a week later.
Ryan	A ghost?
	That would mean she was dead.
Jess	Yeah. She must have been dead.
	And the best bit of the story is that
	her ghost still haunts the house.
	Spooky, eh?
Ryan	Yeah. Spooky.
	Wow! A haunted farmhouse
	with a secret passage!
	I think that's really cool.
	Wait 'til we get home
	and tell everybody.
Jess	There's more.
	The book tells us where
	the secret passage is.
Ryan	Where?

Jess   It leads off the dining room.
          It's behind the wooden panels.

Ryan Right. Let's check it out.

Jess   You told Mum
          we were going to bed.

Ryan We will
          – when we've found the passage.
          You're not scared, are you?

Jess   NO I AM NOT!
          Let's go!

*They leave the living room
and go into the dining room.*

Act 2

In the dining room . . .

Ryan How do we find it?

Jess We tap on the walls.
That way we can tell
if they're hollow.
If they sound hollow,
we should find a passage behind.

Ryan OK. Let's try it.

They begin to tap the wall.

Jess Over here, Ryan. I think I've got it.
It sounds hollow.

Ryan Let me try.

***Ryan** taps the wall.*

You're right, Jess. It must be hollow.
So now we have to find a way in.

Jess	Easy! Look.
	There's a catch down here.
	If I press it ...
	(*she presses the catch*)
	It should open. YES!
Ryan	A black hole.
	Cobwebs and mouse droppings!
	Yuk!
	These old places are something else!
Jess	Get a torch, Ryan.
Ryan	What?
Jess	Don't you want to go inside?
	Don't you want to find out
	where the passage goes to?
Ryan	Yeah. I suppose so.
Jess	Then get the torch. Go on.

Ryan goes out of the room and comes back with a torch.

Ryan I'm not sure this is a good idea.
I could be watching telly
or something.

Jess No you couldn't. There isn't a telly.
I think you're
just scared of the dark.
Or are you scared of ghosts?

Ryan No way!
I don't even believe in ghosts!

Jess Well, come on, then.

*They bend low and step through the
door of the passage.*

Ryan What a stink!
There must be rotting rats in here.

Jess Maybe it's a body!
Maybe we'll find Annie's body
rotting in the passage.

Ryan I'm going to be sick.

Jess Shut up and keep going.

Pinch your nose if you have to.

It could get worse.

The passage is beginning

to drop down here.

Watch your step.

Ryan It's all right for you.

You've got the torch.

I'm behind you.

I can hardly see a thing back here.

Jess It's not so easy for me either.

The torch isn't all that good.

I think the battery must be old.

Ryan That battery's new.

I put it in myself last week.

Jess Well, the light isn't very bright.

I can hardly see.

In fact, it seems to be fading.

Ryan   Fading?
You're kidding! It can't be.
Let's turn back before it goes out.
I don't want to be stuck down here
in the dark.
(*the torch goes out*)
Oh no! The battery's packed in.
HELP! MUM!
COME AND HELP US!

Jess   There's nobody here, Ryan.
What's the point of shouting?
Just turn round.
We can feel our way back.
It's not that far.

Ryan   Right ... I'm ... turning ...
round ...
and ... AAGGGHHH!

Jess   What now?

Ryan   I ... I ... can ...

Jess   WHAT?

Ryan I can see something.

Jess What can you see?

Ryan A glow.

Jess What glow?

Ryan I don't know. It's just a glow.

And it's getting bigger.

Jess ...

Jess What?

Ryan I think it's a g-ghost?

Jess Oh yeah! So why can't I see one?

Ryan C-come here, Jess.

Look here.

You'll see it.

Jess pushes past her brother.

Jess Where? Move over, Ryan.

Oh ... Wow! I ... I can't believe it.

I can see it.

It's glowing brighter and brighter.

I can see ... a girl carrying a candle.

Ryan Who is it?

Jess I don't know – but I can guess!
It's that girl who nicked
the farmer's silver – Annie Harris.

Ryan Do you think so?

Jess Remember what the book said.
Annie Harris came back
to haunt the farmhouse.

Ryan You could be right.
But why is she crying?

Jess I don't know, Ryan.
She's just standing there.
Why won't she let us pass?

Ryan Jess. I'm scared. Really scared.
Have you seen her neck. Look at it.

Jess (*gasps*)
No! No it can't be!
This is terrible!
It's blood.

Ryan It looks as if Annie Harris
was murdered.

Jess   Ryan, look! She's nodding her head.
I think she heard us.
She's nodding ...
She's pulling something
out of her pocket.
What is it?

Ryan   It's a piece of paper.

Jess   No – it's a photograph.
But I can't see what's on it.

Ryan   Hold it out, Annie!
Hold it so we can see it.
That's it!

Jess   It's a photograph of a man.
I've seen him before.
He's in one of the photographs
on the living room wall.
It's Matthew Roberts.

Ryan   Who's he?

Jess   Don't you remember?
He married the rich widow
who owned the farm!

Ryan	I bet he murdered Annie.
Jess	Look! She's nodding.
Ryan	But what's she doing now – holding the picture over the candle? (*he covers his eyes*) I can't stand it! The light's too strong.
Jess	Turn away, Ryan. Don't look!
Ryan	Jess … I'm feeling dizzy.
Jess	Me too. Ow! My head's really hurting. Come on. Let's get out of here.

They run out of the passage.

Act 3

Back in the dining room.

Ryan Oh that's better.
I don't know what happened in there
but I'm glad to be out.

Jess My head still feels funny.
Did you see what I saw
or was I dreaming?

Ryan Dreaming? No way, Jess.
We saw Annie Harris as clear as day.

Jess Then let's go back to the living room
and check out that picture.
Let's see if that photo
was Matthew Roberts.

Ryan Right. Come on.

1908

They return to the living room
and look at the old photo.

Jess   This has to be him.
He's the one in the photo
Annie showed us.

Ryan   It must be him with his wife.
Look. There's the date on the
bottom.
1908, the year they were married.

Jess   Two years before Annie died.

Ryan   He looks like
an ordinary kind of bloke.
Why would he kill her,
do you think?

Jess   It's got to be something to do with
the money.
Maybe he spent the money
on a horse race.

Ryan   Or maybe he lost a fortune
playing cards ...

Jess Maybe his wife would go crazy
if she found out.
Maybe she'd kick him out.
It was her farm, remember.

Ryan Yeah! He'd lose his home.
He'd be poor again.
So he put the blame on Annie.
He said she took the money
– and everybody believed him.
Poor Annie.

Jess Well, we can make sure
everybody knows the truth now.

Ryan How?

Jess We'll write the story
– everything we know.
We'll send it to the papers.
That way Annie's name
will be cleared.
The whole world will know about
Matthew Roberts.

Crash of thunder
and the lights go out.

Ryan Jess! What's happening?
Jess I think it's a p-power cut!
Ryan Then why are you shaking?
Jess B-because I'm scared
that it's more than a power cut.
Ryan Are you th-thinking
what I'm th-thinking?
Jess Are you th-thinking
there's more than one ghost?
Ryan Yes! I am. I think
Matthew Roberts has come back
to take his revenge on us.
Jess Me, too!

Another crash of thunder.

Ryan & Jess *(running out of the room)*
HELP!